I wish I had a rocket...

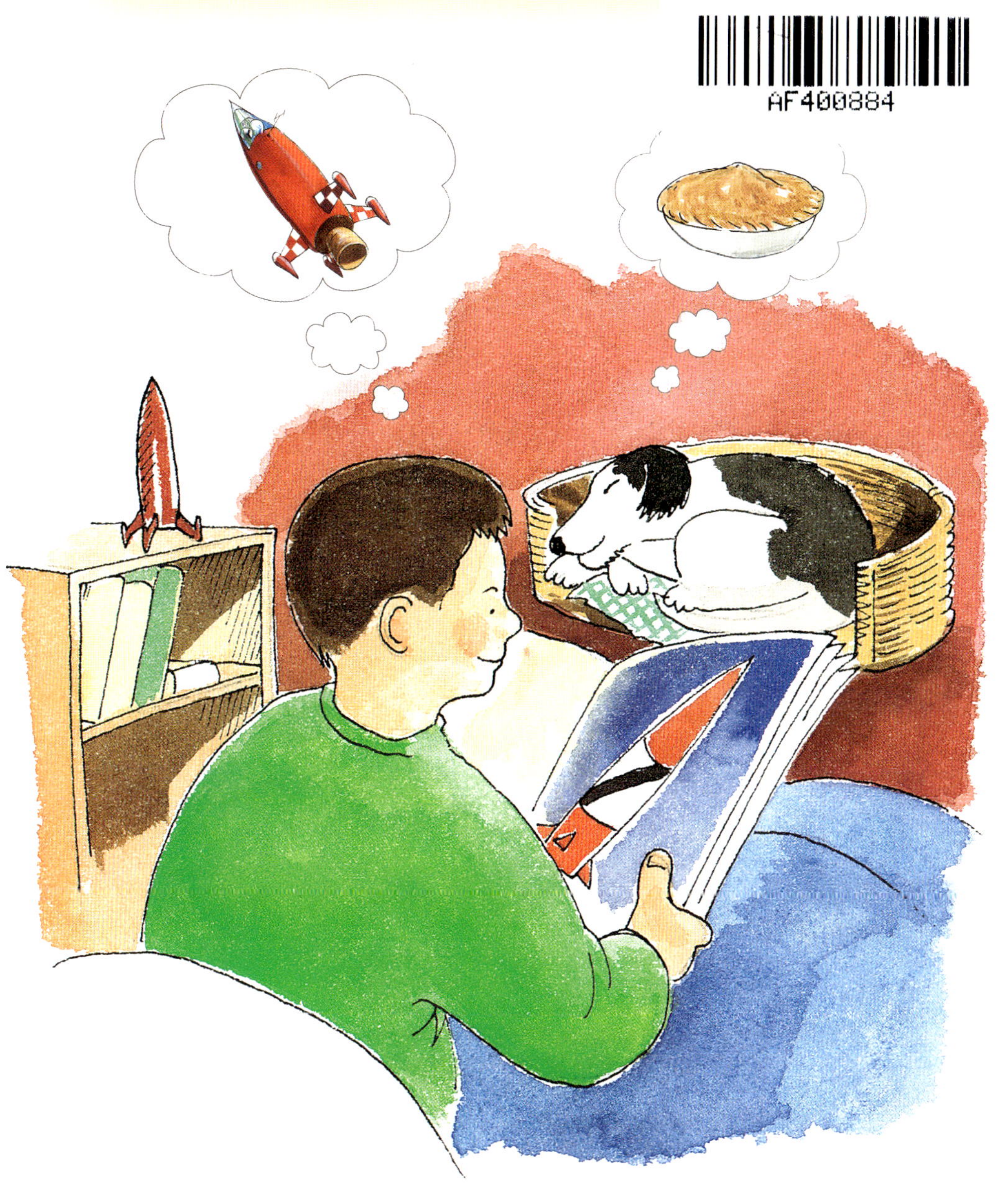

to zoom up to the clouds

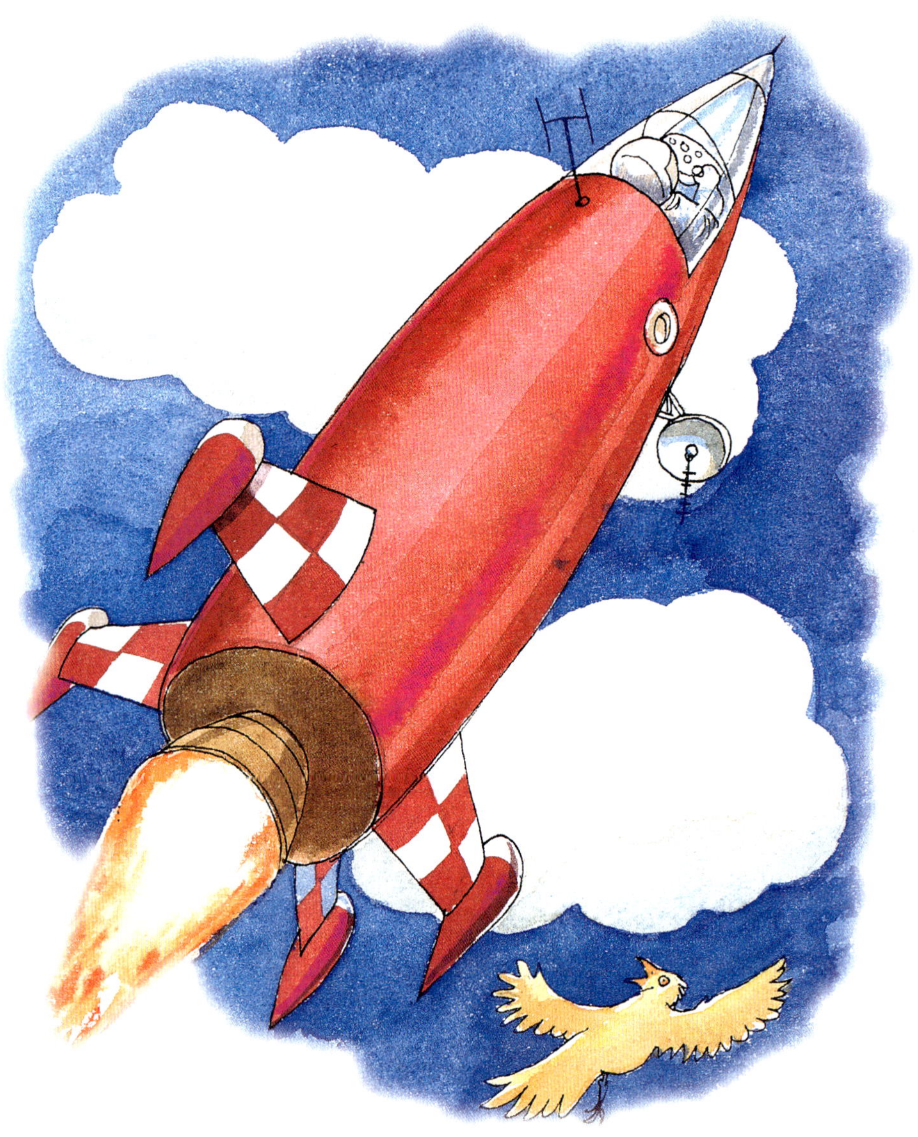

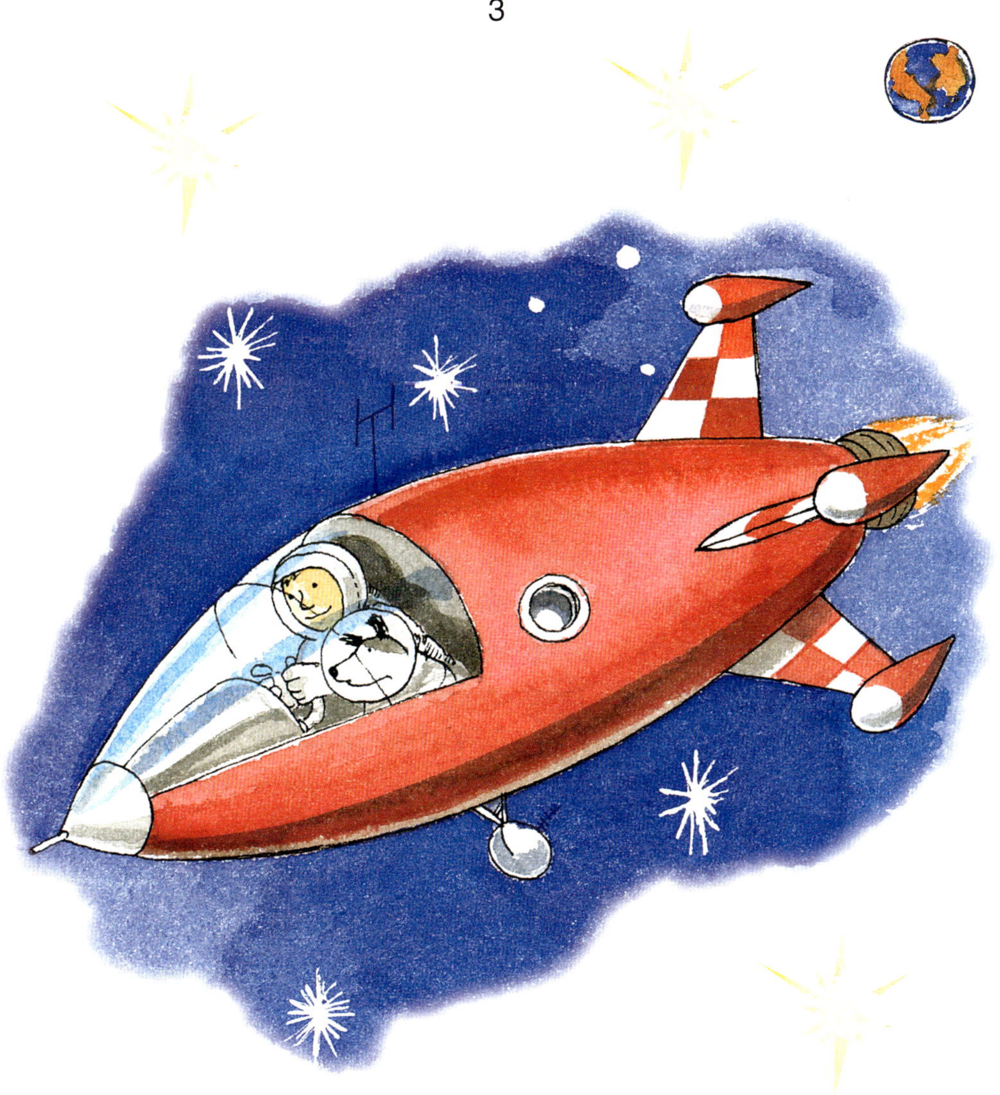

and jet around the stars
a bit...

and land on Planet Mars,

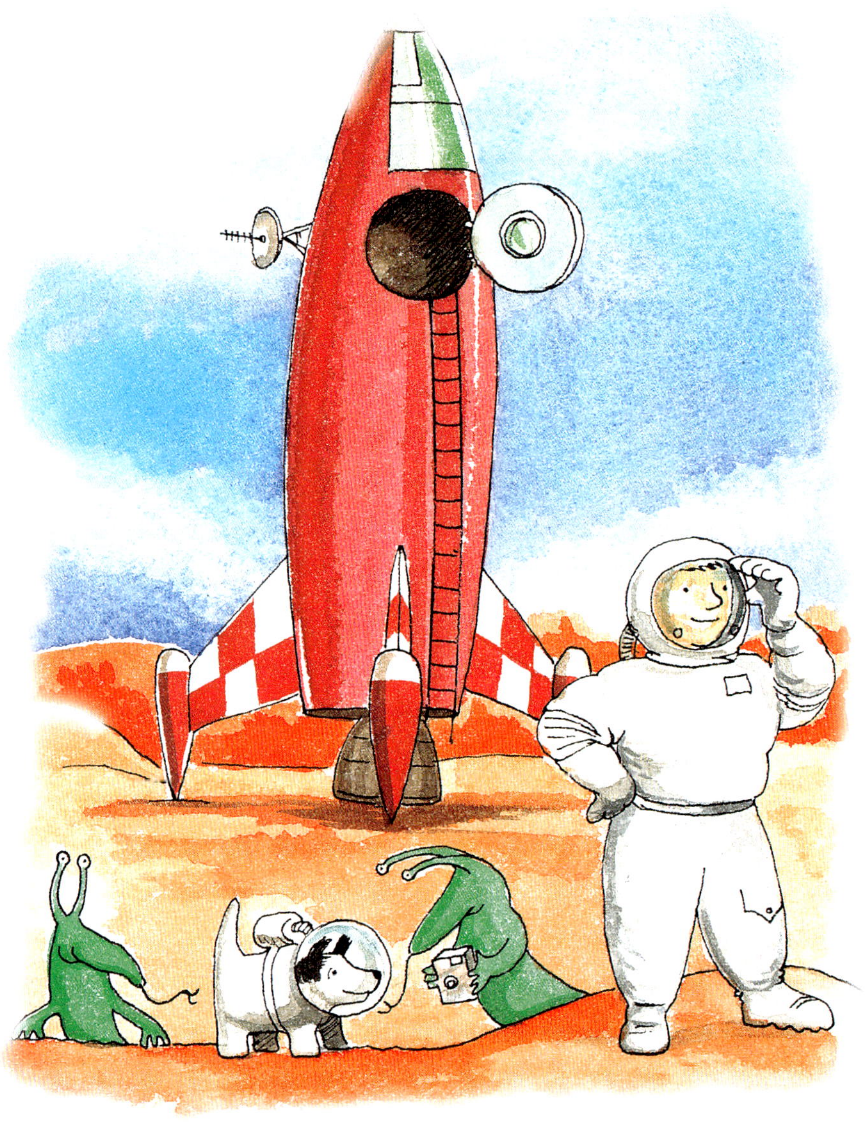

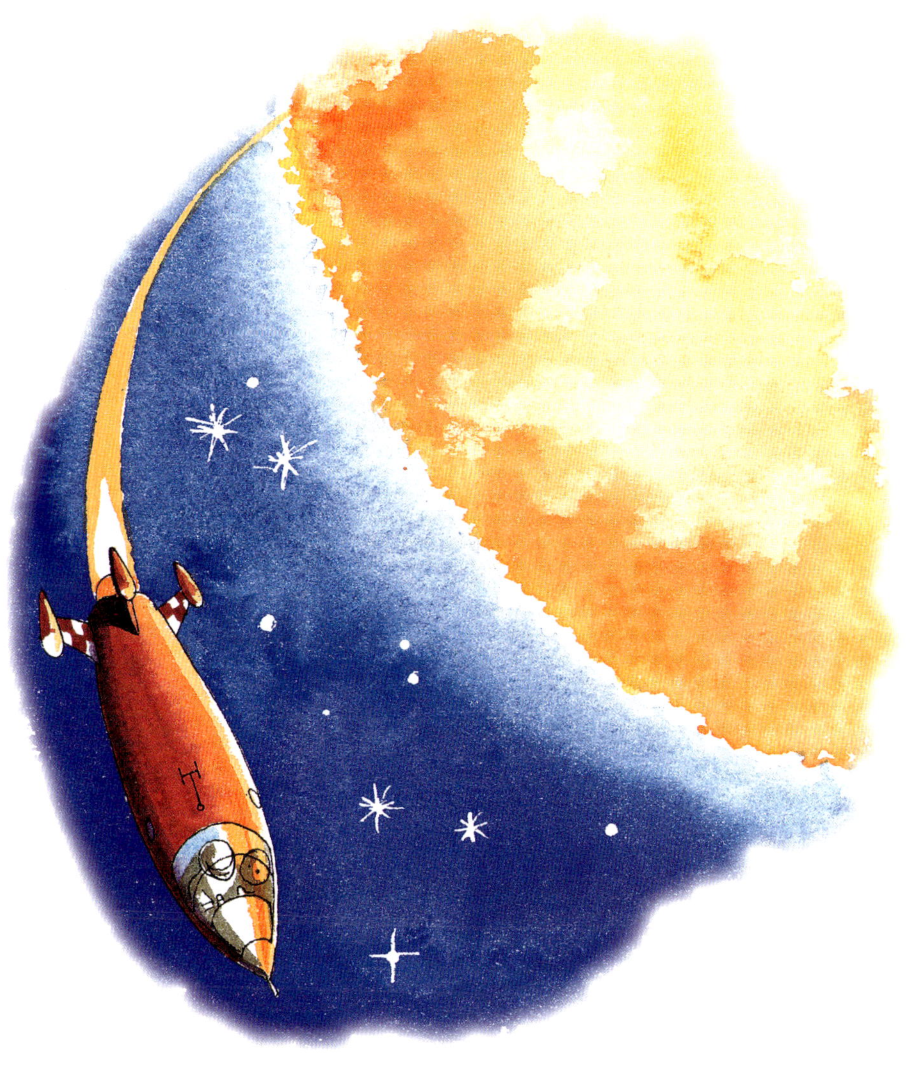

then orbit
around the sun...

until it got too hot

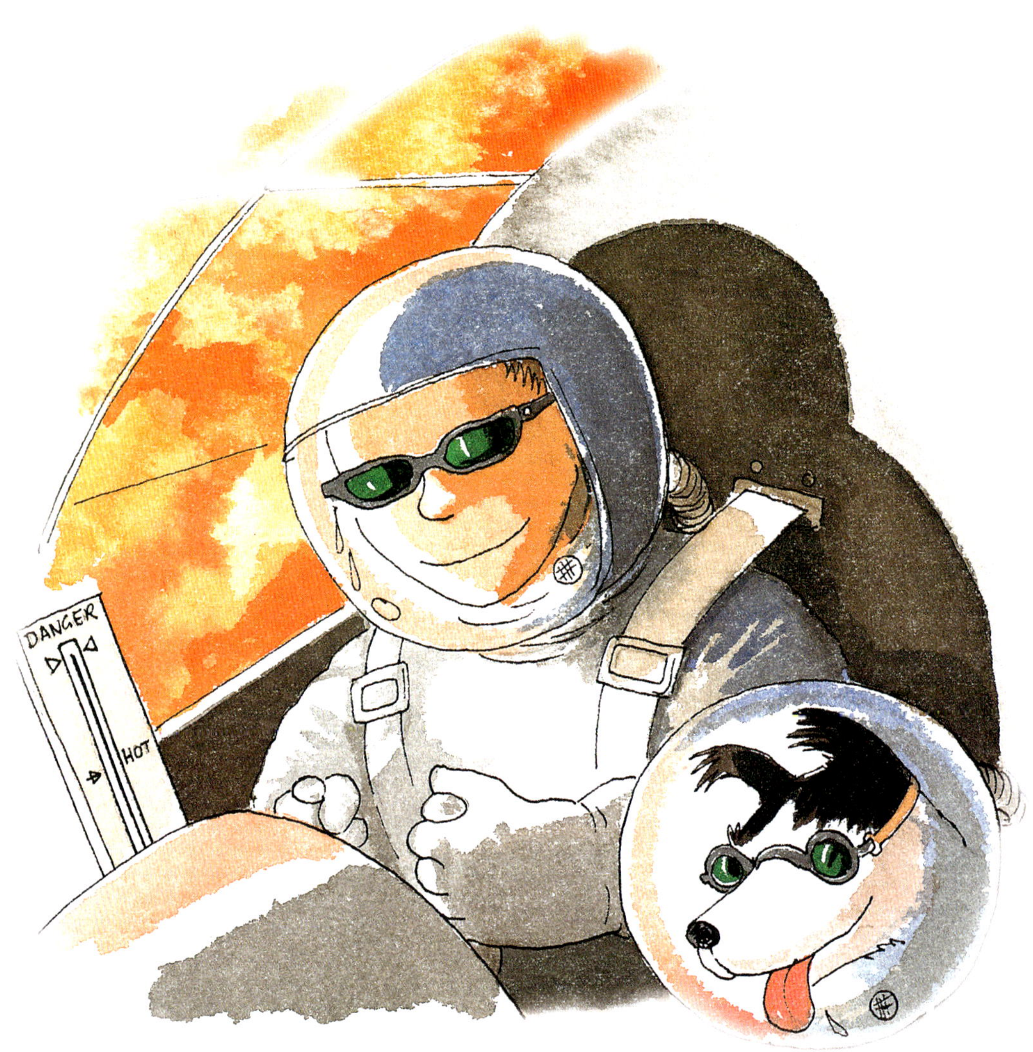

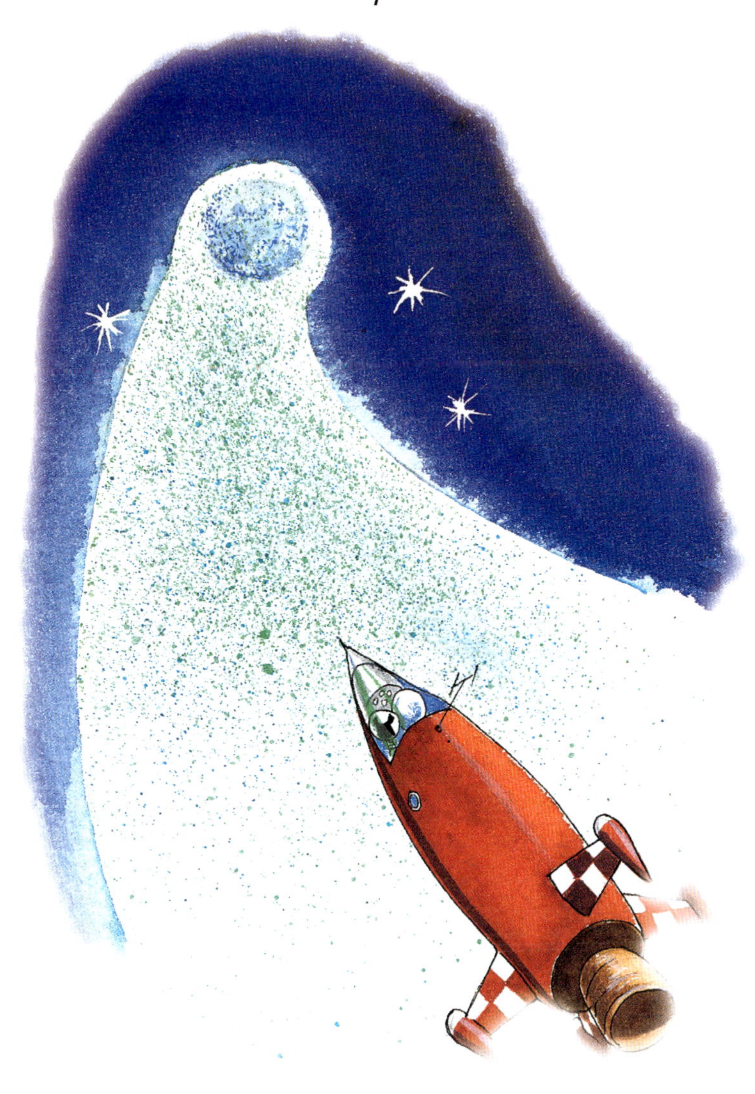

and swoop back on a
comet's tail...

...for a picnic

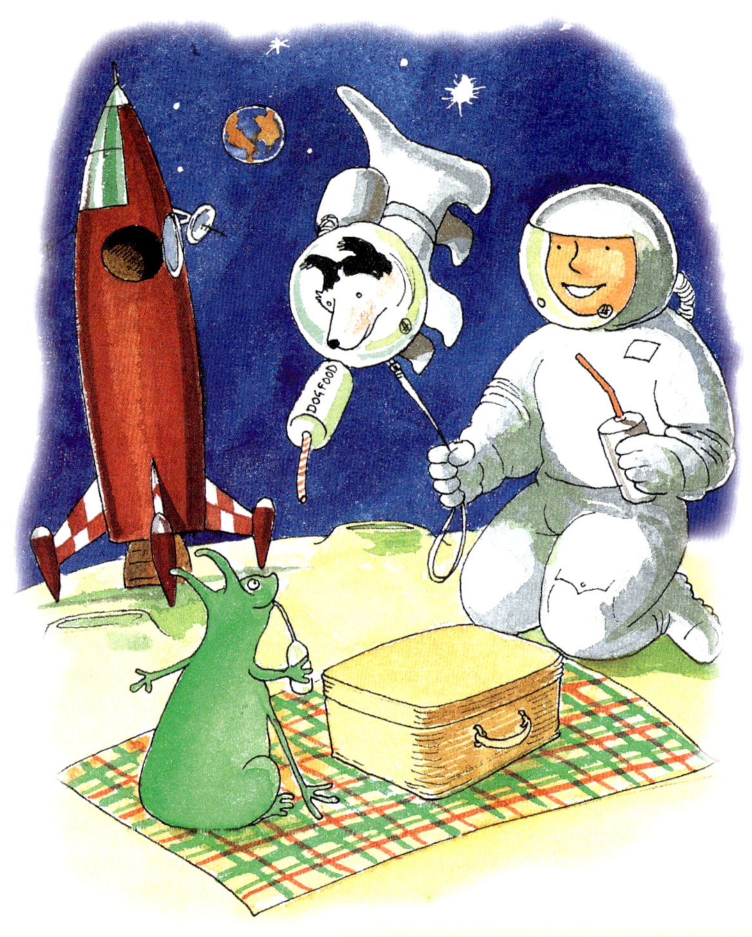

on the moon!